W9-AYI-153

SPOT the DIFFERENCE

PaPP™
publishing

www.pappinternational.com

Art Director: Tammy Desnoyers
Design: Rafaela Petel Ruiz
Images: © Shutterstock

PAPP International Inc.
3700 Griffith Street, Suite 395,
Montreal (Quebec), Canada H4T 2B3

ONE TREE PLANTED

A portion of the proceeds from the sale of this book goes toward reforestation and the Million Tree Challenge.

www.onetreeplanted.org

PUZZLE 3
FIND THE 9 CHANGES & KEEP SCORE

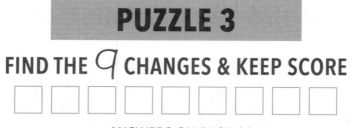

☐ ☐ ☐ ☐ ☐ ☐ ☐ ☐ ☐

ANSWERS ON PAGE 30

ONE OF THESE IS NOT LIKE THE OTHERS, CAN YOU SPOT THE DIFFERENCE ?

ANSWER ON PAGE 30

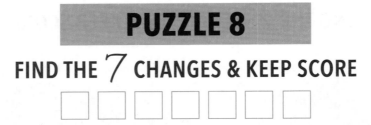

PUZZLE 8

FIND THE 7 CHANGES & KEEP SCORE

☐ ☐ ☐ ☐ ☐ ☐ ☐

ANSWERS ON PAGE 31

ONE OF THESE IS NOT LIKE THE OTHERS, CAN YOU SPOT THE DIFFERENCE ?

ANSWER ON PAGE 31

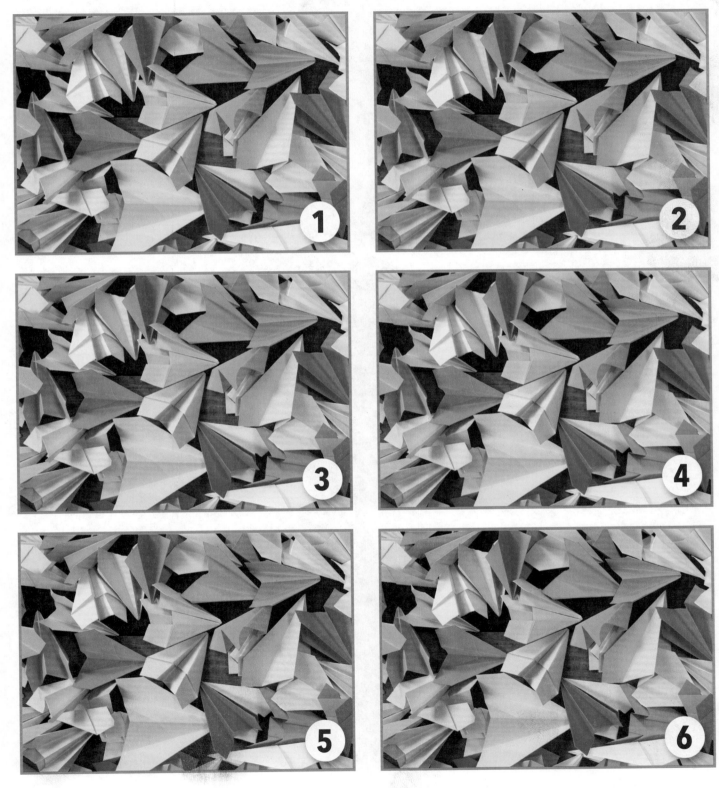

PUZZLE 13

FIND THE 10 CHANGES & KEEP SCORE

☐ ☐ ☐ ☐ ☐ ☐ ☐ ☐ ☐ ☐

ANSWERS ON PAGE 32

PUZZLE 14

ONE OF THESE IS NOT LIKE THE OTHERS, CAN YOU SPOT THE DIFFERENCE?

ANSWER ON PAGE 32

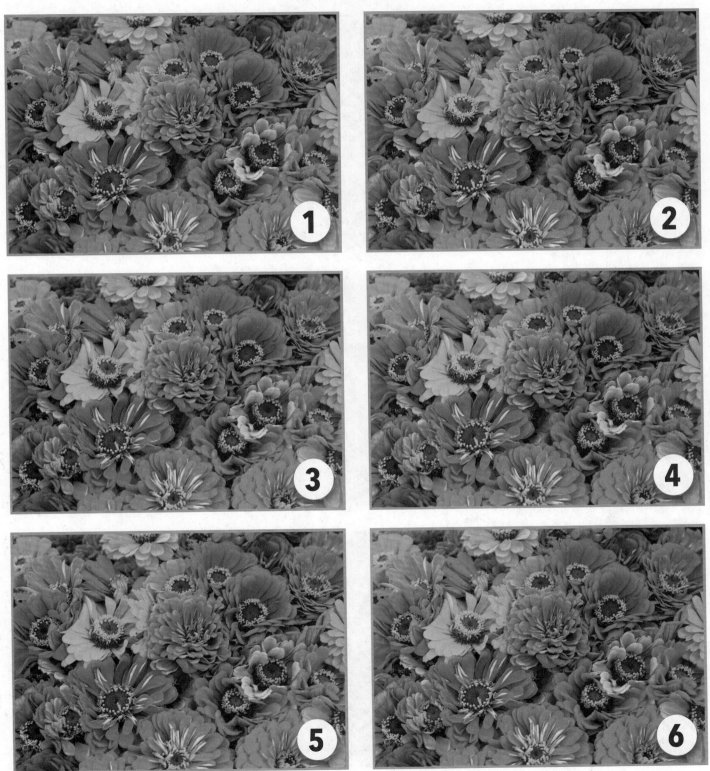

ANSWERS

PUZZLE 1 | **Page 3**

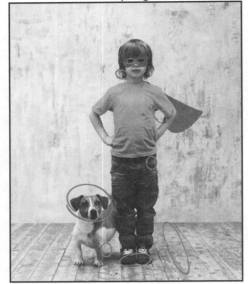

PUZZLE 2 | **Page 5**

PUZZLE 3 | **Page 6**

PUZZLE 4 | **Page 7**

PUZZLE 5 | **Page 9**

PUZZLE 6 | **Page 11**

PUZZLE 7 | **Page 13**

PUZZLE 8 | **Page 14**

PUZZLE 9 | **Page 15**

PUZZLE 10 | **Page 17**

PUZZLE 11 | **Page 19**

PUZZLE 12 | **Page 21**

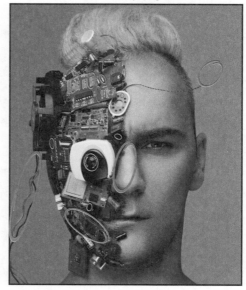

SPOT THE DIFFERENCE ANSWERS • 31

PUZZLE 13 | **Page 22**

PUZZLE 14 | **Page 23**

PUZZLE 15 | **Page 25**

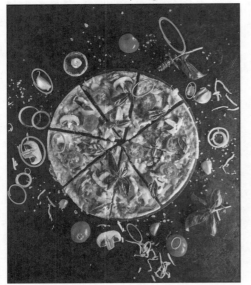

PUZZLE 16 | **Page 27**

PUZZLE 17 | **Page 29**